HEADACHE

KICKSTART

LOS ANGELES · CALIFORNIA

HEADACHE

Created by **LISA JOY**

Art by **JIM FERN**

Colors by **OSCAR MANUEL MARTIN**

Lettering & Design by **BILL TORTOLINI**

Edited by **JIMMY PALMIOTTI**

Produced by **KICKSTART COMICS INC.**

For Kickstart Comics Inc:
Samantha Shear, Managing Editor

Address correspondence to: Kickstart Comics Inc.
480 Washington Ave., North Suite 201, Ketchum, ID. 83340

INTRODUCTION

"Headache" has that magic ingredient, the one I'm always hooked by — the idea that there's something weird hidden underneath the normal world; something smirking down there, tracing patterns on the surface, waiting to come out and play.

The story is a little bit of all of Lisa's favorite things — banter and body blows exchanged in equal measure. And an ass-kicking, wisecracking heroine finding a crack in the sidewalk, hauling it up and discovering that there's a trick to the world; that the social contract is a forgery; and that something older and vainer and angrier has really been running things all this time. And, of course, they're her family.

I'm not going to brag too much about my wife's writing. It'd be unseemly. And redundant — read on and enjoy it for yourself. Suffice to say, as usual, I'm dead jealous. As for inspiration, I'll take her word for it that there's no trace of our home life in the dysfunction on Olympus Drive. And I have no idea where she got the idea for that ass-kicking, wisecracking brunette. None whatsoever.

Jonathan Nolan
(THE DARK KNIGHT, THE PRESTIGE, MEMENTO)

BIRTHDAY

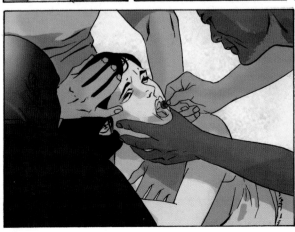

BYGONES

WELCOME TO THE FAMILY, ATHENA!
EVERYBODY WHO'S ANYBODY ON OLYMPUS WILL BE HERE. EXCEPT APOLLO. HE'S GOT A MOVIE PREMIERE.
What have I gotten myself into!
YO, HEPHAESTUS. YOU THINK YOU CAN FORGE THE WORDS "SEA GOD" INTO MY SURFBOARD, DUDE?
HOW CAN I THINK ABOUT FORGING WHEN MY WIFE IS MAKING OUT WITH ARES!
PERSEPHONE, WHAT THE HELL IS SHE DOING HERE.
ATHENA'S NOT SO BAD, DIANA. YOU'RE JUST JEALOUS CUZ APOLLO HAD A CRUSH ON HER. AND YOU'VE SO GOT THE HOTS FOR YOUR BRO.
FEEL LIKE A QUICKIE WITH THE GODDESS OF LOVE, ARES?
I'D RATHER WATCH WAR COVERAGE.
I CAN'T BELIEVE I FAILED AGAIN, DEMETER.
WHO NEEDS A DRIVER'S LICENSE - YOU CAN FLY, HERMES!
TOO MUCH FLAPPING. IT'S EXHAUSTING!
MORE, MORE, MY MAENADS.

Welcome to the family reunion from hell. But these people are my only shot at learning about my past. Where I came from. Who I am.

HI, HUBBY!

PERSEPHONE? YOU'RE MARRIED?

TECHNICALLY. I COULDN'T DEAL WITH MY MOM'S SUPER OVERPROTECTIVE EARTH MOTHER CRAP SO I SNUCK INTO HELL, ATE SOME POMEGRANATE AND TA-DA -- I'M QUEEN OF THE UNDERWORLD AND MOM-FREE FOR HALF OF EVERY YEAR.

DEAD ROSES? FOR ME? YOU SHOULDN'T HAVE.

DEMETER WAS SUPER PISSED ABOUT IT. SHE CURSED HADES SO ALL PLANTS DIE AT HIS TOUCH.

WAIT. THAT'S HADES?

More like nightmarey. So this is Thanatos' boss. The monster behind my mother's death and the attempt on my life.

DREAMY, HUH?

WELL, WELL... LOOK WHO FLEW OVER THE CUCKOOS NEST.

YOU DESERVE THEM, HERA.

Stay calm, Athena. Pick your battles.

On second thought, screw calm. I pick this battle!

ATHENA --

GO AWAY.

PLEASE, ATHENA. DON'T SHUT ME OUT. WE'RE FAMILY.

FAMILY? *YOU DRUGGED ME AND LOCKED ME IN AN INSANE ASYLUM. YOU AREN'T MY FAMILY.* THE ONLY FAMILY I HAD WAS MY MOTHER, AND YOU LET HADES KILL HER!

IT'S NOT HADES' FAULT, OR MINE. WHEN HERA DISCOVERED THE AFFAIR, SHE DEMANDED YOUR MOTHER'S HEAD. NO ONE WAS STRONG ENOUGH TO DEFY HER.

YOU COULD HAVE TRIED! YOU *WOULD* HAVE IF MY MOTHER MEANT ANYTHING TO YOU!

SHE MEANT EVERYTHING TO ME. THAT'S WHY I SAVED HER.

YOU SAVED HER? WHERE?

HERE. YOU SEE, AS GOD OF LIGHTNING, I DON'T JUST CONTROL THE WEATHER. I CONTROL ALL ELECTRICAL CURRENTS. AND WHAT IS MEMORY, BUT A SNAP OF ELECTRICITY? NEURONS FIRING IN THE RECESSES OF YOUR MIND.

IN HERE SHE IS ALWAYS ALIVE, ALWAYS YOUTHFUL, FULL OF LOVE AND VIBRANT.

SHOW ME.

SHOW ME.

HERA WOULDN'T LIKE IT IF I --

I need to remember more! Must hold on!

LET GO!

I SAID, LET GO!

Ever been hit by lightning? It's like every cell in your body explodes with light and sound and pain.

And then? Silence. Peace. Like going home...

It's 431 B.C. Athens.

This was the golden age of democracy, art, philosophy, and science.

This was where we ruled.

STAR-CROSSED

I WORRIED SHE'D WANT TO SAVE MANKIND. TURNS OUT, SHE JUST WANTS HOT POCKETS, AND HIGH DEF CABLE.

SCREW RELIGION. *TV* IS THE OPIATE OF THE MASSES.

What do you do when you realize your parents are planning Armageddon but you have no idea how to stop them?

You seek illumination.

And who better to provide it than the God of Light?

Apollo...

BRAD LIGHT, THE GOLDEN GOD OF THE SILVER SCREEN, IS HERE TO PROMOTE HIS NEW MOVIE "SHOWDOWN". TELL ME BRAD, IS IT TRUE YOU NEVER LIE?

I'M CONSTITUTIONALLY INCAPABLE OF IT.

But I'll have to get by his sister, Artemis... or Diana... whatever she's going by nowadays.

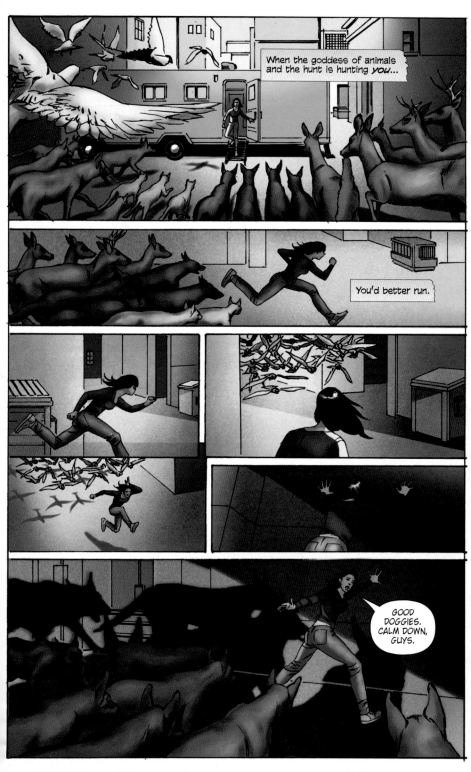

THAT'S RIGHT MY PETS....

... SHE'S JUST WHERE I WANT HER.

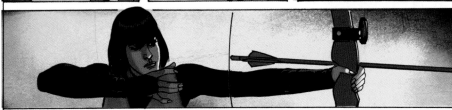

I WON'T LET YOU HURT HER.

YOU CAN'T STOP ME.

DON'T MAKE ME FIGHT YOU.

WHY? AFRAID TO HIT A GIRL?

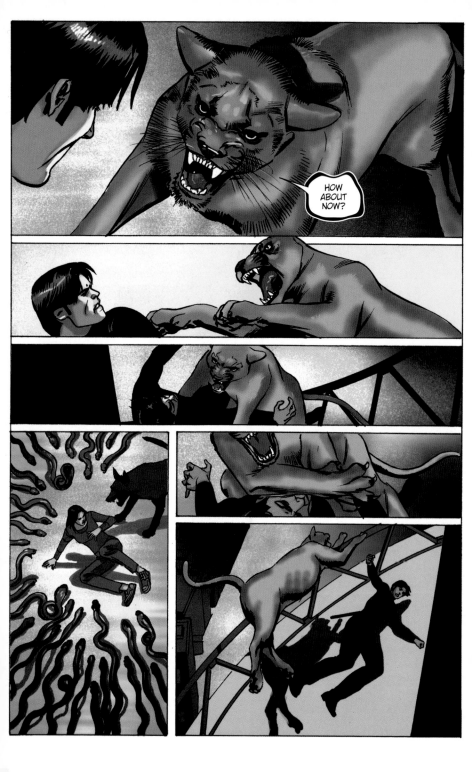

WHAT DO YOU SEE IN HER? SHE HATES DEATH, LOSS, PAIN -- EVERYTHING YOU STAND FOR.

MAYBE THAT'S WHAT I SEE IN HER.

THEN YOU AND I HAVE SOMETHING IN COMMON. WE'RE BOTH IN LOVE WITH SOMEONE WHO WOULD NEVER GIVE US A SECOND LOOK. NOT IN A MILLION YEARS.

Diana would never call her animals off. It's almost like someone was helping me.

Like I'm not...

All alone.

CAN'T
GET YOU
OUT OF MY
HEAD

THANK YOU FOR MEETING ME, MR. KISHIKAWA.

IT IS MY PLEASURE. SEVERAL OF MY FRIENDS HAVE RAVED ABOUT YOUR SERVICES. THEY SAY YOUR REPUTATION AS A "GODDESS OF LOVE" IS WELL EARNED.

CUPID CORP. GUARANTEES SATISFACTION TO ITS CUSTOMERS.

S SOMETHING E MATTER, MR. KISHIKAWA?

IT IS UNCANNY. YOU LOOK JUST LIKE MY WIFE. SHE DIED YEARS AGO BUT...

I GET THAT A LOT.

FINDING A WOMAN AS WONDERFUL AS HER IS HARD.

I KNOW. BUT "CUPID" IS AN ELITE MATCHMAKING SERVICE. WE REPRESENT MODELS, MOGULS, MOVIE STARS. THE KIND OF PERSON A MAN OF YOUR STATURE WOULD BE COMPATIBLE WITH.

ONE CONCERN. I AM A PUBLIC FIGURE IN JAPAN. I WORRY ABOUT... APPEARANCES.

MY SERVICE IS 100% DISCRETE. THERE'S ONLY ONE COPY OF OUR CLIENT LIST AND I KEEP IT WITH ME AT ALL TIMES...

RIGHT NEXT TO MY HEART.

YOU HAVE YOURSELF A DEAL.

WONDERFUL. NOW IF YOU'LL EXCUSE ME...

I HAVE OTHER BUSINESS TO ATTEND TO...

HEPHAESTUS IS WORKING DOWNSTAIR SO I'M ALL YOURS.

DID YOU MISS ME, ARES?

I NEVER MISS ANYONE, APHRODITE. EVEN YOU.

MAKE LOVE, NOT WAR...

OW.

IF YOU WANT GENTLE, GO TO YOUR HUSBAND.

This is a nightmare...

... the same nightmare I've had every night since recovering my memories.

A place of beauty...

Then, in an instant...

Everything's lost.

I know he's coming...

Death.

But I'm not afraid...

IT WAS YOU ALL ALONG.

Not at all.

Just a nightmare. Doesn't mean anything. Not. Anything.

No time to dwell. I've got an assassination to stop. Zeus is brainwashing Twigs to do his dirty work.

I can't punish her for the sins of the father, specifically my father.

So I'll take the fight to Zeus and Hera.

But to beat the Gods, I need focus...

Training...

And a whole lotta weapons.

And for that, I need...

...Aphrodite's husband... Hephaestus.

22 Lovers Lane.

ATHENA?

Will the nightmare ever end?

WHAT ARE YOU DOING HERE?

I COULD ASK THE SAME OF YOU.

WHY WOULDN'T I BE HERE? IT *IS* MY HOUSE.

APHRODITE? IS THAT YOU?

WHY? WHO DID YOU THINK I WAS?

IT DOESN'T MATTER. I'M HERE TO SEE HEPHAESTUS. WHERE IS HE?

WHO KNOWS? WHO CARES? I'VE BEEN WITH ARES.

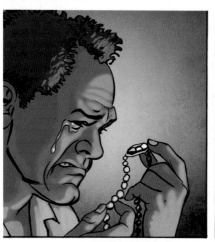

HEPHAESTUS, I NEED WEAPONS. PREFERABLY OF THE GOD-KILLING-ARMAGEDDON-STOPPING VARIETY THAT ONLY YOU ARE ABLE TO MAKE.

SORRY. I CAN'T HELP YOU. MY WIFE SUPPORTS ARMAGEDDON AND I CAN'T BETRAY HER.

EVEN WHEN ALL SHE DOES IS BETRAY YOU? SHE ONLY VOTED FOR ARMAGEDDON TO PLEASE ARES.

BE THAT AS IT MAY, THIS IS NOT MY BATTLE.

THEN **MAKE** IT YOUR BATTLE. THE GODS ARE PLANNING TO KILL MILLIONS OF HUMANS!

PERHAPS, PERHAPS NOT. I DON'T PRESUME TO UNDERSTAND ZEUS' PLAN. KILLING MANKIND BECAUSE HE'S THREATENED BY THE INTERNET SEEMS UNLIKE HIM. HE DIDN'T EVEN BLINK WHEN THE PRINTING PRESS WAS INVENTED.

THERE'S SOMETHING MORE GOING ON HERE, AND I DON'T WANT ANY PART OF IT.

FINE. I GUESS I'M ON MY OWN.

A simple dinner knife. Not enough to kill a God. But enough to do what needs to be done.

Time to visit an old friend.

My old stomping grounds.

Elysian Fields Asylum.

Getting in and out is a lot easier when I'm not doped up on Ambrosia.

SHUT UP! SHUT UP! PLEASE. STOP TALKING.

TWIGS? IT'S ME. SARAH.

TWIGS DOESN'T LIVE HERE ANYMORE.

ARES! PLEASE STOP!

APHRODITE, I WAS HOPING YOU'D COME. I HAVE SOMETHING FOR YOU.

HEPHAESTUS. YOU HAVE TO GET OUT OF HERE.

DO YOU LIKE IT?

WE DON'T HAVE TIME FOR THIS. ARES IS GOING TO CRUSH YOU SO YOU CAN'T MAKE ANY MORE WEAPONS!

HERE. LET ME HELP YOU PUT IT ON.

LISTEN TO ME! THEY'RE GOING TO KILL YOU!

LET THEM. I HAVE NOTHING TO LIVE FOR.

YOU'RE CRYING.

THOSE AREN'T MY TEARS...

...THEY'RE YOURS.

GO NOW. MY POWERS ARE FADING. I DON'T WANT YOU TO SEE ME LIKE THIS. I'M NOT SOME GREAT BEAUTY. NO HELEN OF TROY OR MARILYN MONROE, OR WHOEVER IT IS YOU SEE...

YOU THINK I DON'T SEE YOU, BUT I SEE WHO YOU REALLY ARE. NOT THE FACE YOU SHOW THE WORLD, OR THE FACE YOU SEE IN THE MIRROR, BUT THE THING UNDER EVEN THAT -- YOUR SOUL.

PLEASE...

LOOK AT ME NOW. DO YOU SEE HOW WRONG YOU WERE?

Another day closer to Armageddon. I have nothing. No weapons. No allies. No hope. I've failed.

I'll go to Hephaestus one last time. If he won't give me a weapon... I'll take one.

22 Lovers Lane.

WHAT THE --

APHRODITE! APHRODITE WAIT!

HUH?

ARE YOU TALKING TO ME?

WHO ELSE WOULD I BE TALKING TO?

UM... I THINK THERE'S A LITTLE CONFUSION HERE...

CONFUSION? MORE LIKE TOTAL MAYHEM. WHAT HAPPENED TO YOUR HOUSE?

THE INSURANCE ADJUSTERS WOULD CALL IT AN "ACT OF GOD", AND THEY'D BE RIGHT.

THANK GOODNESS YOU WEREN'T HURT.

I DIDN'T KNOW YOU CARED ABOUT ME.

COURTING DEATH

YOU'LL NEVER BEAT ZEUS AND HERA. YOU CAN'T EVEN BEAT A CRIPPLE. YOU'RE JUST...

NOT READ--

-EEE EEEE...

I'M SO SORRY, YOUR BAD LEG. I CAN'T BELIEVE I --

NOW. YOU'RE READY.

ZEUS AND HERA ARE STRONGER THAN YOU. TO BEAT THEM, YOU HAVE TO ATTACK THEIR VULNERABILITIES. FIND THEIR WEAKNESSES AND EXPLOIT THEM.

HOW? THEY DON'T HAVE WEAK LEGS.

NO, BUT THE FLESH IS WEAK IN MORE WAYS THAN ONE. APHRODITE KNEW THAT. HER LITTLE BLACK BOOK COULD BE THE KEY TO TAKING DOWN YOUR DAD.

THE VOICE. SO LOUD. LIKE THUNDER. LIKE AN ITCH I CAN'T SCRATCH.

Elysian Fields Asylum.

I CAN'T BELIEVE I'M SAYING THIS, BUT... YOU'RE FREE TO GO.

GOD SENT FOR ME. JUST LIKE HE PROMISED.

SEE YOU IN HELL.

54 Olympus Drive.

THAT'S RIGHT, CHILD. GO NOW. DO MY BIDDING.

MY ACOLYTE IS FREE.

IT'S AMAZING WHAT FRIENDS IN HIGH PLACES CAN DO FOR YOU.

TIME TO CELEBRATE?

NOT NOW, HERA.

LATELY YOU'RE NEVER IN THE MOOD. THERE'S NOT SOMEONE ELSE, IS THERE?

OF COURSE NOT. I'M JUST EXHAUSTED FROM PLANNING ARMAGEDDON. BUT AS SOON AS WE WIPE OUT THE HUMAN RACE, I'M ALL YOURS. PROMISE.

BEFORE YOU GO IN THERE, YOU SHOULD KNOW. APHRODITE HAS A LONG WAYS TO GO BEFORE SHE'S STRONG ENOUGH TO RE-ENTER THE OUTSIDE WORLD. SHE'S A LITTLE... SENSITIVE ABOUT HER CONDITION.

PLEASE, JUST BE CAREFUL.

SORRY... I'LL JUST, UH. BE OUT HERE.

APHRODITE?

GO AWAY, ATHENA!

NOT UNTIL YOU HELP ME!

I NEED YOUR LITTLE BLACK BOOK.

TO BEAT THE GODS, I NEED TO EXPLOIT THEIR VULNERABILITIES. MY FATHER'S ONE WEAKNESS WAS ALWAYS WOMEN.

HEPHAESTUS TOLD ME TO FIND YOU--

HEPHAESTUS IS HELPING YOU? THE GODS WILL KILL HIM!

SINCE LOSING YOU, HE DOESN'T CARE.

HE SHOULD.

DEATH MAY BE TEMPORARY FOR THE GODS, BUT IT'S STILL HELL.

DID YOU GET WHAT YOU CAME FOR?

YOU *MONSTER!*

THIS IS WHAT THE AFTERLIFE IS? THE PAIN? THE TERROR? IS THIS WHAT YOU PUT MY MOTHER THROUGH?

APHRODITE DID A LOT SHE'S NOT PROUD OF. HER SUFFERING IS HER WAY OF ATONING.

YOUR MOTHER IS IN A FAR DIFFERENT, PEACEFUL PLACE. I MADE SURE TO TAKE CARE OF HER. JUST LIKE I TRY TO TAKE CARE OF YOU.

I VISITED APOLLO WHERE DIANA TRIED TO KILL ME, YOU WERE THERE, WEREN'T YOU?

YES.

WHY DID YOU SAVE ME?

ISN'T IT OBVIOUS?

IT WAS YOU ALL ALONG.

I'm not afraid. Not at all.

MR. SWAN TOLD ME TO COME HERE.

I'VE BEEN EXPECTING YOU.

IT WILL MAKE A PRETTY HOLE IN A PRETTY HEAD.

THIS IS WEIRD, ISN'T IT?

UNEXPECTED, MAYBE. BUT GOOD, RIGHT?

I DON'T MEAN "US". I MEAN THIS. APHRODITE SAID MY FATHER WENT BY "MR. SWAN".

BUT THERE HASN'T BEEN ONE ENTRY WITH HIS NAME ON IT IN THE LAST CENTURY!

MAYBE HERA SCARED HIM STRAIGHT.

SHE ALMOST KILLED HIM LAST TIME HE STRAYED. I DOUBT HE'LL DO IT AGAIN WHILE SHE'S ALIVE.

THAT'S IT!

I'VE BEEN LOOKING IN THE WRONG PLACE.

GOTCHA.

WHAT WAS THAT FOR?

FOR FIGURING OUT HOW TO SAVE THE WORLD.

STAY BEHIND THE TAPE. CLEAR A PATH FOR THE PRESIDENT.

I HEAR NOTHING BUT YOUR VOICE, ZEUS. LIKE THUNDER IN MY HEAD. COMMAND ME. GUIDE ME.

IS THE PRESIDENT GOING TO WAVE?

YES, SWEETHEART. HE'LL PASS RIGHT IN FRONT OF HERE WITH HIS WIFE.

HERE, HISTORY WILL BE MADE. I MUST STAND HERE.

HEY -- WE'VE BEEN WAITING HERE FOR HOURS. FIND YOUR OWN SPOT TO --

MOVE.

54 Olympus Drive.

HOW ARE YOU, MY LOVE?

TWIGS IS IN POSITION. SHE'LL HAVE A CLEAR SHOT.

GOOD. POSEIDON, ARES AND I WILL STAND GUARD TO MAKE SURE NO ONE INTERRUPTS YOU.

AND IF ATHENA RETURNS AND TRIES TO STOP ME?

I'LL KILL HER.

SO YOU TWO ARE... *TRAINING* TOGETHER?

I CAN HELP YOU FIGHT OFF POSEIDON AND ARES.

AND HADES IS THE ONLY ONE WHO CAN KEEP ZEUS AND HERA TRAPPED IN HELL.

FIRST WE HAVE TO SEND THEM THERE.

THIS WON'T BE EASY. EVEN THOUGH A GOD NEVER TRULY *DIES*, YOU'LL BE SENDING THEM TO HELL FOR A LONG TIME.

ARE YOU REALLY READY TO TAKE DOWN YOUR OWN PARENTS?

AS READY AS I'LL EVER BE.

THERE GOES THE NEIGHBORHOOD.

I ALWAYS KNEW THAT FAMILY WAS TROUBLE.

POLICE SPECULATE THE ACCIDENT ON OLYMPUS DRIVE COULD HAVE RESULTED FROM A METH LAB EXPLOSION.

THERE ARE BELIEVED TO BE NO SURVIVORS.

MY GOD! IT'S IMPOSSIBLE!